# The Irresistible

## JiM DAViS

RR
RAVETTE PUBLISHING

First published by
Ravette Publishing Limited 1997

Printed and bound in Great Britain
for Ravette Publishing Limited,
Unit 3, Tristar Centre,
Star Road, Partridge Green,
West Sussex RH13 8RA
by Cox & Wyman Ltd, Reading, Berkshire

ISBN 1 85304 940 9

JIM DAVIS 12-30

© 1985 PAWS, INC./Distributed by Universal Press Syndicate

WHAT A BEAUTIFUL, SUNNY DAY!

YOU ARE A DOLT. YOU ARE UGLY, AND YOU ARE GENERALLY UNACCEPTABLE

THEY LOVE ATTENTION

© 1995 PAWS, INC./Distributed by Universal Press Syndicate

WHAT ARE YOU GOING TO DO? GUM ME?

BEWARE THE

© 1995 PAWS, INC./Distributed by Universal Press Syndicate

THAT GEEZER'S LETHAL WITH A CANE

JIM DAVIS 2-3

© 1995 PAWS, INC. Distributed by Universal Press Syndicate

CLICK

© 1995 PAWS, INC./Distributed by Universal Press Syndicate

EIGHTEEN HOURS, NINE MINUTES

ROLL ME OVER. I CAN DO BETTER!

JYM DAVYS 2-8

AAARGHH

JIM DAVIS 2-25

SO HOW DID YOU DO ON YOUR DIET?

LET'S JUST SAY I WON'T BE WEARING BIKINI BRIEFS TO THE BEACH ANYTIME SOON

© 1995 PAWS, INC./Distributed by Universal Press Syndicate

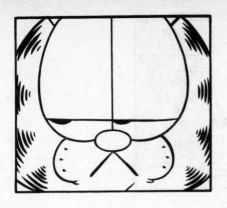

I CAN WAIT, BIRD

© 1995 PAWS, INC./Distributed by Universal Press Syndicate

SOONER OR LATER, YOU'VE GOTTA COME OUT OF THERE AGAIN

JIM DAVIS 3-14

TWIST

© 1995 PAWS, INC./Distributed by Universal Press Syndicate

JIM DAVIS 3-15

CREAM IN YOUR COFFEE, GARFIELD?

JIM DAVIS 3-16

I'M SORRY! DID I OFFEND YOUR SENSE OF AESTHETICS?!

Cream

ATTENTION! STEP AWAY FROM THE BURGER! STEP AWAY FROM THE BURGER!

WOOP WOOP WOOP WOOP

A BURGER ALARM!

AH-HA

JIM DAVIS 3-18

THE CAPTAIN APOLOGIZES FOR THE SLIGHT TURBULENCE

© 1995 PAWS, INC./Distributed by Universal Press Syndicate

JIM DAVIS 3-25

THIS ALSO CONCLUDES THE MEAL PORTION OF YOUR FLIGHT

SH☉NK

© 1995 PAWS, INC./Distributed by Universal Press Syndicate

JIM DAVIS 4·4

MOW THE LAWN!

© 1995 PAWS, INC./Distributed by Universal Press Syndicate

JIM DAVIS 4-15

© 1995 PAWS, INC./Distributed by Universal Press Syndicate

© 1995 PAWS, INC./Distributed by Universal Press Syndicate

C'MON, MOUSE... LET GO!

SAY "PRETTY PLEASE WITH A CHERRY ON TOP"

JIM DAVIS 4·22

LOUSY WEATHER
WE'RE HAVING

© 1995 PAWS, INC./Distributed by Universal Press Syndicate

NOT IF YOU DON'T
GET OUT OF BED!

JIM DAVIS 4-24

© 1995 PAWS, INC./Distributed by Universal Press Syndicate

JIM DAVIS 4-26

JIM DAVIS 4-27

© 1995 PAWS, INC./Distributed by Universal Press Syndicate

© 1995 PAWS, INC./Distributed by Universal Press Syndicate

## OTHER GARFIELD BOOKS IN THIS SERIES

| No.  1 | Garfield The Great Lover | £2.99 |
|---|---|---|
| No.  2 | Garfield Why Do You Hate Mondays? | £2.99 |
| No.  3 | Garfield Does Pooky Need You? | £2.99 |
| No.  4 | Garfield Admit It, Odie's OK! | £2.99 |
| No.  5 | Garfield Two's Company | £2.99 |
| No.  6 | Garfield What's Cooking? | £2.99 |
| No.  7 | Garfield Who's Talking? | £2.99 |
| No.  8 | Garfield Strikes Again | £2.99 |
| No.  9 | Garfield Here's Looking At You | £2.99 |
| No. 10 | Garfield We Love You Too | £2.99 |
| No. 11 | Garfield Here We Go Again | £2.99 |
| No. 12 | Garfield Life And Lasagne | £2.99 |
| No. 13 | Garfield In The Pink | £2.99 |
| No. 14 | Garfield Just Good Friends | £2.99 |
| No. 15 | Garfield Plays It Again | £2.99 |
| No. 16 | Garfield Flying High | £2.99 |
| No. 17 | Garfield On Top Of The World | £2.99 |
| No. 18 | Garfield Happy Landings | £2.99 |
| No. 19 | Garfield Going Places | £2.99 |
| No. 20 | Garfield Le Magnifique! | £2.99 |
| No. 21 | Garfield In The Fast Lane | £2.99 |
| No. 22 | Garfield In Tune | £2.99 |
| No. 23 | Garfield The Reluctant Romeo | £2.99 |
| No. 24 | Garfield With Love From Me To You | £2.99 |
| No. 25 | Garfield A Gift For You | £2.99 |
| No. 26 | Garfield Great Impressions | £2.99 |
| No. 27 | Garfield Pick Of The Bunch | £2.99 |
| No. 28 | Garfield Light Of My Life | £2.99 |
| No. 29 | Garfield Hangs On | £2.99 |
| No. 30 | Garfield In Training | £2.99 |
| No. 31 | Garfield Says It With Flowers | £2.99 |
| No. 32 | Garfield Wave Rebel | £2.99 |
| No. 33 | Garfield Let's Party | £2.99 |
| No. 34 | Garfield On The Right Track | £2.99 |
| No. 36 | Garfield The Gladiator | £2.99 |

| Garfield's How To Party Book | £2.99 |
|---|---|
| Garfield's Big Fat Book Of Jokes & Riddles | £2.95 |
| Garfield The Me Book | £2.99 |
| Garfield Address Book and Birthday Book Gift Set | £7.99 |
| Garfield Address Book | £4.99 |
| Garfield Birthday Book | £2.99 |

| A Garfield Christmas | £3.99 |
| Garfield's Thanksgiving | £2.95 |

## GARFIELD THEME BOOKS

| Garfield's Guide to Behaving Badly | £3.99 |
| Garfield's Guide to Insults | £3.99 |
| Garfield's Guide to Pigging Out | £3.99 |
| Garfield's Guide to Romance | £3.99 |

---